Disney
FAIRIES

TinkerBell
AND THE
GREAT FAIRY RESCUE

pi kids

phoenix international publications, inc.

Summer is the busiest season of the year, and Tinker Bell can't wait to start tinkering! But Clank has just spilled a load of tinker supplies. Help the tinkers find these things that they will need:

this bucket

this barrel

this saw

this spool of wire

this hammer

this spring

this ruler

When Tinker Bell and Vidia walk near the humans' house, they discover another house that is just their size. Tink rushes in to explore. Look for these candies that she finds:

Lizzy has loved fairies for as long as she can remember! She shows her drawings to Tinker Bell to find out if her fairies look anything like the fairies Tink knows. Look around Lizzy's room to find these fairies that she drew:

Tinker Bell is fascinated by Lizzy's dollhouse. It's like a human house, but it's just the right size for fairies! Search the rooms to find some of Tink's favorite things:

pillow

vase

rocking chair

painting

mirror

stool

When Tink decides to repair the leaks at Lizzy's house, she looks for supplies in the attic. Find these things she might use:

a kettle

a wrench

this bottle

this piece of pipe

a hammer

a funnel

this can

twine

Tink's friends come to rescue her, and they almost get caught by Mr. Twitches! The rain made their wings too wet to fly, so they need these items to build a bridge:

this plate

this bowl

this saucer

this bowl

this cup

this plate

When Lizzy practices flying for the first time, her room gets very messy! Sort through her things to find some of her best-loved toys in the clutter:

this teddy bear

this toy horse

this stuffed rabbit

this doll

this baby doll

this stick horse

this kite

Lizzy's father didn't believe in fairies—until he met Tinker Bell. Now, he even has tea parties with them! Search for these treats that are just the right size for his new friends:

this cake

this cupcake

this tart

this cookie

this pie

this muffin

Go back to the fairies' base camp to find these fairies who have lots to do:

Vidia

Fawn

Rosetta

Silvermist

Iridessa

Bobble

Lizzy used a lot of buttons when she built the fairy house because she knows that fairies love them! Return to the house to find these particular buttons:

Fly back to Lizzy's room to find these fairies:

In the dollhouse, Tink discovers that some things are not what they seem. Hunt for these things that fooled her at first:

Swing back to the attic to find these webs that the resident spider has spun:

Go back to the kitchen to find these houseplants:

When Lizzy practiced flying in her bedroom, she accidentally knocked over her bookcase. Go back to find some of her favorite fairy books:

Flutter back to the tea party to find the fairies' butterfly friends: